I WANT TO BE LIKE MOMMY

By Courtney Scully

Dedicated to my beautiful daughter, Avery. May you shine your light in all that you do in this world.

Mommy is my **EVERYTHING**, Mommy is my **QUEEN**. I hope one day to have her heart and everything in between.

Mommy rocks me back and forth whilst singing an angelic tune. I want to be like Mommy so I can sing like an angel too.

I want to be like Mommy.

I run to Mommy's bed to tell her I've had a bad dream. She pulls me in and hugs me tight. I want to be like Mommy because she isn't afraid of anything.

I want to be like Mommy.

I've fallen down and scraped my knee and tears run down my face as I cry out for her. Mommy comes to kiss my scrape and wipe my tears away. I want to be like Mommy because she makes everything better.

I want to be like Mommy.

Mommy busies herself in the kitchen making us a yummy meal. She's chopping up this and stirring that. I want to be like Mommy so I can cook like that.

I want to be like Mommy.

Mommy puts on her makeup and styles her hair.
I want to be like Mommy and have such flair.

I want to be like Mommy.

Mommy drives off in her car looking cool and free. I want to be like Mommy so I can drive here and there and be wherever I want to be.

I want to be like Mommy.

I go to visit Mommy at work, and I sit in her chair and spin. I want to be like Mommy and be as successful as she has been.

I want to be like Mommy.

I watch daddy grab Mommy's hand and she smiles as big as can be. I want to be like Mommy and find the perfect one for me.

I want to be like Mommy.

I'm about to embark on a new adventure and I think, as always, I want to be like Mommy.

I want to be like Mommy.

As I rock my own new baby girl back and forth and sing to her a tune, I think to myself:
I hope I'm like Mommy.

CPSIA information can be obtained
at www.ICGtesting.com
Printed in the USA
LVHW071427060521
686679LV00016B/454